"H" Is for Holidays

by Annalisa McMorrow
illustrated by Marilynn G. Barr

Dedicated to Kimberly, Marissa, & Raul.

Publisher: Roberta Suid
Design & Production: John Howland
Cover Design: David Hale

Contents

Introduction

H Is for Holidays focuses on historical holidays that introduce children to the history of the U.S.A. through informative and exciting cross-curriculum activities. Holiday-related language, math, art, spelling, homework, and game activities are featured for each week. Songs are also included.

At the start of the school year, help children create their Holiday Portfolios. They can use these to store all of their holiday-related materials in the classroom, or to take items home to share.

Patterns throughout the unit can serve many purposes. For instance, many may be duplicated and used as name tags, or desk or cubby labels. Or enlarge the patterns to use as festive bulletin board decorations.

The activities in *H Is for Holidays* are intended for grades one through three. However, some lessons may easily be simplified for younger children. For instance, if children cannot write their own reports or stories, they can dictate them to the teacher or teacher's helper, record them on a tape recorder for an audio report, or draw pictures to represent the words.

Graphic organizers accompany several language activities. These forms help the children to stay focused on the topics that they are researching.

The unit ends with a final game that allows children to share the knowledge that they've learned. Once children have finished the game, give the students Historian Diplomas (p. 64).

During the school year, search for holiday-related books to store in your reading corner. Children can spend free time learning more about the holidays they're studying, or about additional festive celebrations. Challenge children to search for mentions of holidays in the books and magazines that they read on their own. Also be on the lookout for games, puzzles, and toys with a holiday theme.

The Web is a good place to locate information about holidays to share with the students. Several Web sites are listed below as a starting point. Remember, Web sites change with frequency. Always check the sites yourself before sharing them with the students.

A holiday calendar is included on page six. This calendar lists holidays mentioned in this book, as well as other special days you might want to celebrate with the students. As you learn about other holidays, add them to the calendar. At the end of the year, duplicate a copy of the holiday calendar for the children to keep.

Below are several Web and book resources to use in conjunction with this unit.

Web Sites:
This holiday-related site includes information, facts, craft ideas and more for many different holidays.
http: www.web-holidays.com

This Lincoln site includes photos of Lincoln as well as transcripts of his speeches. It includes pictures of the drafts of the Gettysburg address delivered November, 19, 1863.
http://lcweb.loc.gov/exhibits/gadd

Holiday-related Books:
• *Albert's Thanksgiving* by Leslie Tryon (Atheneum)
• *Lincoln: A Photobiography* by Russell Freedman (Clarion)
• *Yankee Doodle* by Edward Bangs (Aladdin)

Holiday Calendar

January	January 16: Matin Luther King, Jr. Day
February	February 12: Lincoln's Birthday February 22: Washington's Birthday Third Monday: Presidents Day
March	
April	
May	May 31: Memorial Day
June	June 14: Flag Day
July	July 4: Independence Day
August	
September	
October	October 12: Columbus Day
November	November 11: Armistice Day Fourth Thursday - Thanksgiving
December	

Holiday Portfolio

Children will enjoy making festive portfolios in which to store their work.

Materials:
Portfolio Patterns (p. 8), scissors, crayons or markers, glue, hole punch, yarn, legal-sized folders or large sheets of heavy construction paper

Preparation:
Duplicate a copy of the Portfolio Patterns for each child.

Directions:
1. Demonstrate how to make a portfolio. If using legal-sized folders, punch holes along the two open sides. Cut two arm-length pieces of yarn and tie knots in one side of each. Thread the yarn through the holes and tie the free ends together to make a strap. If using construction paper, fold the paper in half to make a folder, and then continue as described above.
2. Give each child a sheet of patterns to color and cut out.
3. Have the children decorate their portfolios with crayons, markers, and the patterns.

Options:
• The children can add their own hand-drawn pictures, as well. Or they can cut out pictures from magazines or used holiday cards to glue to their portfolios.
• Cover the portfolios with contact paper for added sturdiness. Reinforce the holes with hole reinforcers.

Portfolio Patterns

Ship's Log

This activity introduces children to research by having them contribute to a shipboard log. The activity could focus either on the journey of Columbus or the Pilgrims.

Materials:
Ship's Log Organizer (p. 10), Ship's Log (p. 11), encyclopedias, books about Columbus or the Pilgrims, paper, pens or pencils

Preparation:
1. Duplicate a copy of the Ship's Log Organizer and the Ship's Log for each child.
2. Gather encyclopedias for children to use.

Directions:
1. Give each child a graphic organizer.
2. Explain that the children will be using encyclopedias to gather information about the shipboard journey of either Columbus or the Pilgrims.
3. Have the children fill out the graphic organizer, then use the encyclopedia or other resources to gather information.
4. The children can transfer their information to the Ship's Log patterns. They should write the information as if they were part of the journey. For instance, they might write, "We landed in the Bahamas in 1492."
5. Bind the completed entries in a classroom log.

Option:
Duplicate the Columbus and Pilgrim Fact Cards (pp. 13-14) for the children to use for research.

Ship's Log Organizer

Name: _____

Date: _____

I want to learn about: (Circle one.)

Columbus' journey   the Pilgrims' trip

Write three questions that you would like to answer, for instance, "How long was the trip by sea?"

1._____

_____

2._____

_____

3._____

_____

I found out these facts:

1._____

_____

2._____

_____

3._____

_____

Ship's Log

Ship Shape Report

Children will enjoy writing reports on ship-shaped paper. Use the provided fact cards for research, or let children discover facts in encyclopedias or other resource books.

Materials:
Columbus Fact Cards (p. 13), Pilgrim Fact Cards (p. 14), Ship Shape Report (p. 15), encyclopedias, books about Columbus or the Pilgrims, paper, pens or pencils, laminating machine, blue crepe paper, scissors, tape

Preparation:
1. Duplicate enough fact cards for the children to share. Cut out the cards and laminate (if desired).
2. Duplicate a copy of the Ship Shape Report for each child.

Directions:
1. Give each child a Ship Shape Report pattern.
2. Explain that the children will be using encyclopedias, fact cards, and other resources to gather information about Columbus or the Pilgrims. Challenge each child to gather at least three facts.
3. Have the children write brief reports in the space provided on the Ship Shape Report pattern.
4. Post the reports on a bulletin board decorated with blue crepe paper to look like the ocean.

Option:
Younger children can dictate their reports to students from upper grades.

When Columbus died he had almost been forgotten by his people.

In 1493, Columbus sailed with 17 ships to discover Puerto Rico.

On October 12, 1492, Columbus reached Watling Island in the Bahamas.

Columbus was born in 1451 in Genoa, Italy.

Columbus Fact Cards

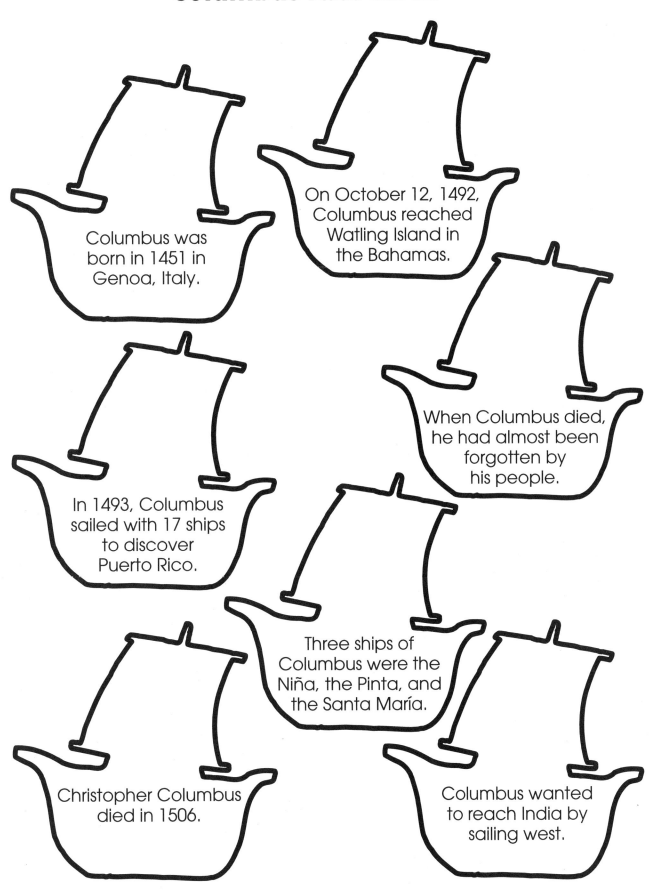

Columbus was born in 1451 in Genoa, Italy.

On October 12, 1492, Columbus reached Watling Island in the Bahamas.

When Columbus died, he had almost been forgotten by his people.

In 1493, Columbus sailed with 17 ships to discover Puerto Rico.

Three ships of Columbus were the Niña, the Pinta, and the Santa María.

Christopher Columbus died in 1506.

Columbus wanted to reach India by sailing west.

Pilgrim Fact Cards

The Pilgrims left England in search of a better life.

The Pilgrims wanted the right to practice their religion freely.

The Pilgrims sailed on a ship called the Mayflower.

The Pilgrims settled in Plymouth, where they had a disastrous winter.

The trip on the Mayflower was long and difficult.

A group of local Native Americans helped the Pilgrims. The Native Americans taught them how to grow corn and other vegetables.

In celebration of the harvest, the Pilgrims and the Native Americans had a three day feast.

In 1863, President Lincoln proclaimed a national day of Thanksgiving.

Ship Shape Report

How Many Ships?

This activity can be used for different levels of mathematical study. For younger children, write a plus or minus sign in the middle box of each equation. Write in a multiplication sign for older children.

Materials:
Ships Ahoy! (p. 17), pencils, crayons or markers

Preparation:
1. Fill in the missing signs (+, -, or x), then duplicate the Ships Ahoy page. Make one for each child.
2. Make an answer key for self-checking, if desired.

Directions:
1. Give each child a copy of the math page.
2. Have the children do the problems and then share their answers with the class. Or they can use the answer key for self-checking.

Options:
• For older children, pass out the math pages without any signs written in the boxes. Let the children make their own problems. They can add a +, -, or x and then write the answers on the back. Have the children trade papers.
• To make the problems more difficult, add more ships or write in larger numerals after the boxes.

Ships Ahoy!

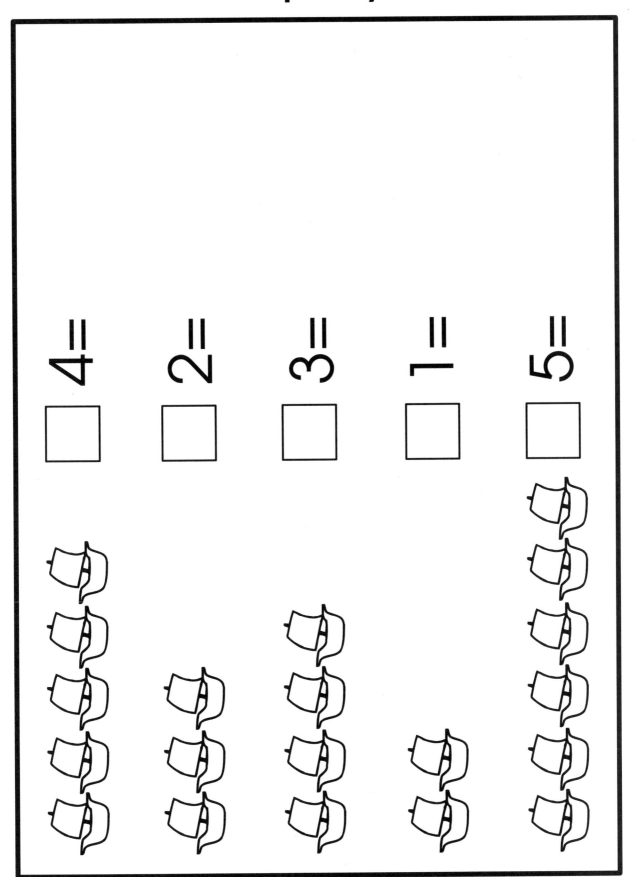

Set Sail for a Spelling Bee

Materials:
Spelling Ships (p. 19), bag, scissors, colored markers, blue construction or crepe paper, tape or glue

Preparation:
1. Duplicate a copy of the spelling words for each child and one for teacher use.
2. Cut the patterns apart and color as desired.
3. Create an ocean-themed bulletin board display using blue construction or crepe paper.

Directions:
1. Announce a date for a spelling "bee."
2. Divide the students into small groups. Have the children work together to learn the words. Let the children take the spelling words home to study.
3. On the day of the spelling bee, put the patterns in a bag. Pull one pattern from the bag at a time and have a child spell the word on the ship.
4. If the child spells the word correctly, he or she can post the ship on the ocean bulletin board. If not, another child tries to spell the word.
5. Continue until each child has a chance to spell one word, and all of the ships are posted on the board.

Options:
• Use the blank ships to make enough words for each child in the classroom to spell at least one.
• If the words are too difficult, white-out the given spelling words and write in your own.

Spelling Ships

India

Italy

Mariner

Navigator

Niña

Pilgrim

Pinta

Santa María

Ship

Turkey Feathers

This cooperative art activity lets children work together to create bulletin board displays.

Materials:
Turkey (p. 21), Feathers (p. 22), tape or glue, pencils or crayons, scissors

Preparation:
1. Enlarge the turkey pattern and color as desired.
2. Duplicate a feather pattern for each child.

Directions:
1. Give each child a feather. On the feather, have the children write (or dictate) something that they are thankful for.
2. Working together, have the children attach the feathers to the back of the turkey pattern. Make sure all of the feathers are readable. (If you have a large class, create several turkey displays.)
3. Post the turkeys in the class where students can enjoy reading them.

Options:
• The turkey and feather patterns can be used to make a wide range of displays. Create a classroom name display by having each child write his or her name on a feather. Attach the feathers to the turkey. Or have each child write one fact about Thanksgiving or Pilgrims on a feather.
• Provide additional decorations, such as dyed feathers, for children to use to make a more festive display.

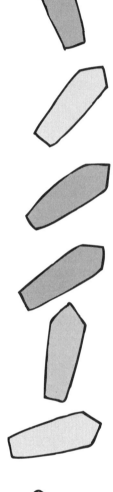

Turkey

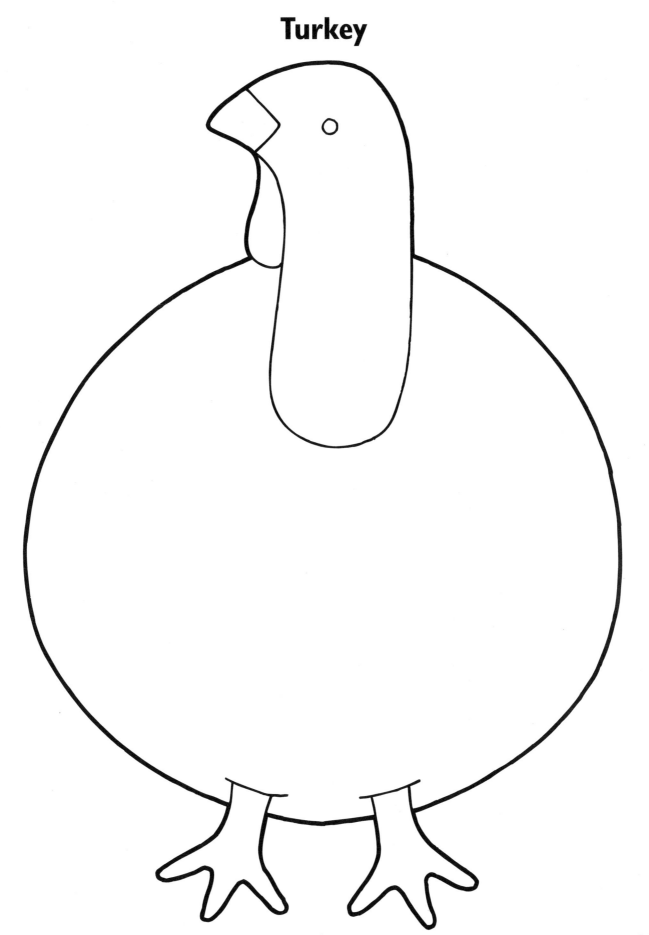

Feathers

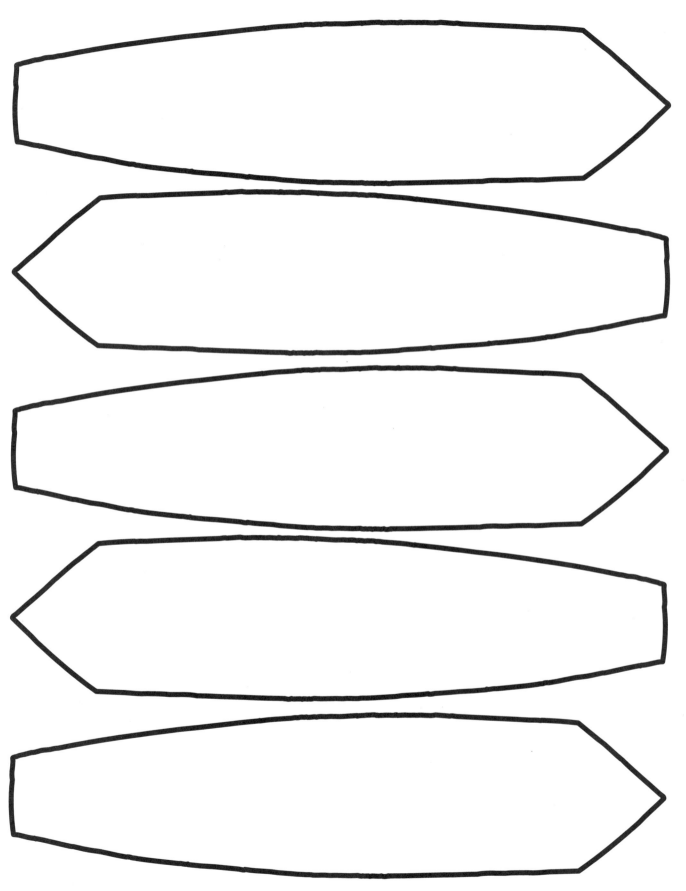

Tape the Tail on the Turkey

This game is a variation on the favorite "Pin the Tail on the Donkey."

Materials:
Turkey (p. 21), Feathers (p. 22), tape, crayons or markers, scissors

Preparation:
1. Enlarge the turkey pattern and color as desired.
2. Duplicate a feather pattern for each child.

Directions:
1. Give each child a feather pattern.
2. Explain the goal of the game: to tape the feather as close to the turkey's tail as possible.
3. Have the children close their eyes (or use a blindfold) as they try to tape the tail on the turkey.
4. Leave all feathers where the children place them.

Options:
• Have a child spin around one or two times before trying to place the tail feather in the right spot.
• Each child can write his or her name on a feather before placing it.
• Children can write Thanksgiving facts on the feathers before taping the feathers to the turkey.

Columbus & Thanksgiving Songs

I Am Very Thankful
(to the tune of "On Top of Old Smokey")

I am very thankful,
In so many ways.
I'm thankful for blue skies
And bright sunny days.
But now that we've studied
The Pilgrims' long trip.
Mostly, I am thankful
Not to be on a ship!

Traditional Columbus Jump Rope Rhyme
Christopher Columbus sailed the ocean blue
      In 1492.
The waves rose higher and higher,
Until over they blew.
And this is what Columbus said to do.
"Bow to the guards. Curtsey to the Queen.
And turn your back on the mean old King!"

H Is for Holidays © 2002 Monday Morning Books

Thanksgiving Books

Children will put together little books about the different things that they, and their families, are thankful for.

Materials:
Book Patterns (p. 26), crayons or markers, scissors, stapler, construction paper

Preparation:
1. Duplicate a copy of the Book Patterns for each child.
2. Cut the construction paper to fit the book pages. Make two sheets per child.

Directions:
1. Give each child a copy of the patterns to cut apart.
2. Help the children assemble their books. They can create front and back covers from colored construction paper.
3. Have the children take their books home. With the help of their families, they should fill in the different things they're thankful for.
4. When the children bring their books into the classroom, they can share their completed books.

Option:
Make a large classroom book of the things that the students are thankful for.

Book Patterns

H Is for Holidays © 2002 Monday Morning Books

Presidential Biographies

Children will take on the role of biographer as they learn about the two presidents we celebrate on Presidents' Day: George Washington and Abraham Lincoln

Materials:
Biography Organizer (p. 28), President Fact Cards (pp. 29-30), encyclopedias, books about Washington and Lincoln, paper, pens or pencils, scissors

Preparation:
1. Duplicate a copy of the organizer for each child and enough fact cards for the children to share. Cut apart the cards.
2. Gather encyclopedias and other resource books for the children to use.

Directions:
1. Give each child an organizer.
2. Explain that the children will be using encyclopedias, biographies, and fact cards to gather information about the presidents.
3. Have the children fill out the organizers, then use encyclopedias and other resources to gather information.
4. The children can use the information that they learn to write brief biographies about their subjects. Post the completed biographies in a "Let's Learn about the Presidents!" display.

Option:
Instead of a presidential biography, children could do a biography for Martin Luther King, Jr., using the fact cards provided (p. 31).

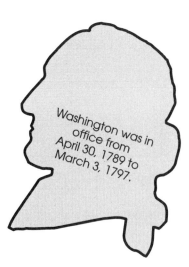

Washington was in office from April 30, 1789 to March 3, 1797.

King was a clergyman and civil rights leader.

Lincoln's Vice Presidents were Hannibal Hamlin (1861 to 1865) and Andrew Johnson (1865).

Biography Organizer

Name:_____

Date: _____

Before writing a biography, a writer needs to learn facts about the subject. Write three questions that you would like to answer about the person you are studying. You might write a question like, "When was President Lincoln born?"

These are the questions that I want to answer.

1._____

_____

2._____

_____

3._____

_____

This is what I found out:

1._____

_____

2._____

_____

3._____

_____

H Is for Holidays © 2002 Monday Morning Books

Washington Fact Cards

George Washington was the first President.

Washington lived from 1732 to 1799.

Washington was in office from April 30, 1789 to March 3, 1797.

Washington's first lady was Martha Washington.

George Washington's Vice President was John Adams.

Lincoln Fact Cards

Abraham Lincoln was the sixteenth President.

Lincoln lived from 1809 to 1865.

Abraham Lincoln was a Republican.

Lincoln was in office from March 4, 1861 to April 15, 1865.

Lincoln's first lady was Mary Todd Lincoln.

Lincoln's Vice Presidents were Hannibal Hamlin (1861 to 1865) and Andrew Johnson (1865).

Martin Luther King Jr. Fact Cards

Martin Luther King, Jr. worked for civil rights.

King staged nonviolent marches, protests, and demonstrations.

Martin Luther King, Jr. was born in Atlanta on January 15, 1929.

King lived from 1929 to 1968.

King was a clergyman and civil rights leader.

King was awarded the 1964 Nobel Peace Prize.

We All Have Dreams

You might read parts of Martin Luther King, Jr.'s famous "I Have a Dream" speech to the children before doing this activity. The transcript can be found on the Web (see link on this page).

Materials:
I Have a Dream pattern (p. 33), crayons or markers, pens or pencils

Preparation:
Duplicate a copy of the pattern for each child.

Directions:
1. Discuss Martin Luther King, Jr.'s "I Have a Dream" speech. Explain that his *dream* was about a time when all people would be treated equally, regardless of their skin color or religious beliefs.
2. Give each child an "I Have a Dream" pattern.
3. Have the children draw pictures of things that they dream about for the future. These could be personal goals for themselves or their families, or the way they hope the world will be when they are older.
4. Gather the pages into a book titled "Our Dreams for the Future."

Option:
Have the children write short pieces to go with their illustrations.

Web Site:
This web site includes transcripts of many of King's famous speeches, as well as a chronology, photographs, and a biography. Audio portions are available, as well.
http://www.stanford.edu/group/King/

H Is for Holidays © 2002 Monday Morning Books

I Have a Dream...

Cherries on a Tree

This activity is based on the famous fable of a young George Washington confessing to cutting down a cherry tree. This story was intended to illustrate his honesty. Use this activity for different levels of mathematical study. For younger children, write a plus or minus sign in the middle cherry of each equation. Write in a multiplication sign for older children.

Materials:
Cherry Tree Math (p. 35), pencils, crayons or markers

Preparation:
1. Fill in the missing signs (+, -, or x), then duplicate the Cherry Tree Math pages. Make one for each child.
2. Make an answer key for self-checking, if desired.

Directions:
1. Give each child a copy of the math page.
2. Have the children do the problems and then share their answers with the class. Or they can use the answer key for self-checking.

Options:
• For older children, pass out the pages without any signs written in the middle cherries. Let the children make their own problems. They can add a +, -, or x and then write the answers on the back. Have the children trade papers.
• To make the problems more difficult, white-out the numerals and write in larger numerals.

H Is for Holidays © 2002 Monday Morning Books

Cherry Tree Math

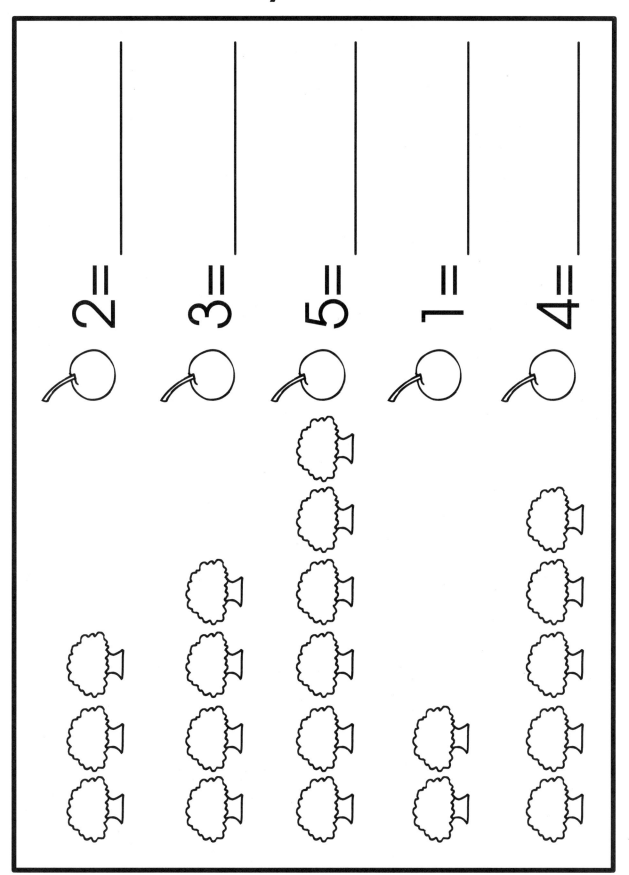

Famous Speech Spelling Bee

Materials:
Word Balloons (p. 37), Speaker Patterns (p. 38) bag, scissors, colored markers, tape or glue

Preparation:
1. Duplicate a copy of the spelling words for each child and one for teacher use.
2. Cut the word patterns apart and color as desired.
3. Enlarge the different patterns of the famous speakers, color as desired, and post on a bulletin board.

Directions:
1. Announce a date for a spelling "bee."
2. Divide the students into small groups. Have the children work together to learn the words. Let the children take the spelling words home to study.
3. On the day of the spelling bee, put the patterns in a bag. Pull one pattern from the bag at a time and have a child spell the word.
4. If the child spells the word correctly, he or she can post the word on the bulletin board. If not, another child tries to spell the word.
5. Continue until each child has a chance to spell one word, and all of the words are posted on the board.

Options:
• Use the blank word balloons to make enough words for each child in the classroom to spell at least one.
• If the words are too difficult, white-out the given spelling words and write in your own.

H Is for Holidays © 2002 Monday Morning Books

Spelling Words

Character

Continent

Dream

Emancipation

Gettysburg

Nation

President

Proclamation

Speaker Patterns

Abraham Lincoln

George Washington

Martin Luther King, Jr.

Presidential Plates

Children can imagine what their own Presidential china pattern would look like.

Materials:
Heavy paper, scissors, tape or glue, crayons or markers.

Preparation:
Cut the paper into circles that are the size of plates. Or let the children do this themselves.

Directions:
1. Have the children observe Lincoln's china pattern.
2. Let the children create their own festive patterns.
3. Post the completed china patterns where the whole class can enjoy them.

Options:
• Have the children create place settings for a Presidential table, from silverware to glassware.
• Provide plain paper plates for children to decorate.

Historical Concentration

This activity uses historical figures in the standard concentration game.

Materials:
Historical Cards (p. 41), paper, crayons or markers, envelopes (one per child)

Preparation:
Duplicate a copy of the cards for each child.

Directions:
1. Give each child a copy of the cards to color and cut out.
2. Teach the children the concentration game, or remind them of the rules. They turn all of the cards face down. Then they take turns flipping two cards over. If the pictures on the cards match, they keep both and try again. If the cards don't match, they turn them face down and another child takes a turn.
3. The children can take the concentration game home to play with their families.

Option:
Older children can practice spelling the names of the people on the cards as they turn over the cards.

George Washington

Martin Luther King, Jr.

Abraham Lincoln

Mary Todd Lincoln

Historical Cards

Abraham Lincoln

Mary Todd Lincoln

Martin Luther King, Jr.

Coretta Scott King

George Washington

Martha Washington

Washington and King Songs

George Washington Never...
(to the tune of "On Top of Old Smokey")

George Washington never
Chopped down any tree.
The tale demonstrated
Young George's honesty.

Martin Luther King
(to the tune of "Row, Row, Row Your Boat")

Martin Luther King
Shared his wondrous view.
Together, together, together, together
We'll make his dream come true!

H Is for Holidays © 2002 Monday Morning Books

Presidential Recipes

Children will work with their relatives to write down their own favorite recipes. If you can cook in the classroom, consider making one of Washington's favorite dishes.

Materials:
Recipe Cards (p. 44), scissors, pens or pencils

Preparation:
Duplicate a copy of the cards for each child and cut them apart.

Directions:
1. Share with the children one of Washington's favorite foods. Then have the children imagine that they have become president. They've been asked to share a recipe for their favorite foods with the rest of the country.
2. Have the children take home the blank recipe card to fill in with their families. They should write the directions for making their own favorite homemade foods on the cards.
3. When the children bring the cards back to the class, duplicate enough for each child to have a classroom recipe book.

Option:
Have the children bring in their favorite foods to share in a classroom potluck.

Fun Facts:
George Washington's favorite foods included beefsteak and kidney pie, trifle, and chess cake (see recipe on the next page). Abraham Lincoln's favorite foods included scalloped oysters, chicken, and election cake.

Presidential Recipe Cards

Chess Cakes (Bake this with a grown-up helper!)

Ingredients: 1 cup butter, 1 cup sugar, 6 egg yolks (beaten),
1/3 cup water, 1 tablespoon lemon juice, grated rind of 1 lemon,
1/4 teaspoon salt, pastry for one 9-inch pie or 12 tarts (use a muffin tin)

Directions:
1. Cream butter and slowly beat in 1/2 cup sugar.
(Save the rest of the sugar.)
2. Beat the egg yolks with salt until they are light and lemon covered.
Slowly, add the remaining 1/2 cup sugar. Use a whisk to fold in the lemon
juice and lemon rind.
3. Combine with the creamed mixture, stirring in the water.
4. Pour the mixture in a pie shell or tart shells. Bake at 350 degrees
Fahrenheit for 50-60 minutes until set.

 H Is for Holidays © 2002 Monday Morning Books

Decoration Day Report

Memorial Day, first known as Decoration Day, is a holiday meant to honor and respect fallen soldiers.

Materials:
Flag Fact Cards (p. 46), Flag Report pattern (p. 48), pens or pencils, crayons or markers, resource books and encyclopedias, crepe paper (red, white, and blue), tape

Preparation:
1. Duplicate a copy of the report pattern for each child.
2. Duplicate and cut apart enough fact cards for children to share.
3. Gather books about Memorial Day.

Directions:
1. Give each child a report pattern.
2. Explain that the children will be using encyclopedias, books, and fact cards to gather information about Memorial Day.
3. Have the children gather facts and then write short reports on the flag patterns.
4. Post the completed reports on a bulletin board as tribute to our fallen soldiers. Decorate the board with red, white, and blue crepe paper.

Options:
• Have the children make flag poles from straws or craft sticks. They can attach the flag reports to the poles, flying the flags at half-mast. (This means that the flags are halfway up the flagpole. This is an indication of mourning.)
• Children can use the Independence Day Facts (p. 47) to create reports for Independence Day.

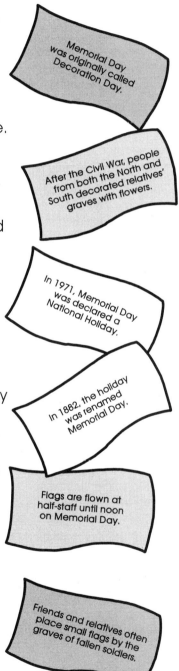

Memorial Day was originally called Decoration Day.

After the Civil War, people from both the North and South decorated relatives' graves with flowers.

In 1971, Memorial Day was declared a National Holiday.

In 1882, the holiday was renamed Memorial Day.

Flags are flown at half-staff until noon on Memorial Day.

Friends and relatives often place small flags by the graves of fallen soldiers.

Decoration Day Flag Facts

In 1971, Memorial Day was declared a National Holiday.

Decoration Day was originally observed on May 30, 1868.

Friends and relatives often place small flags by the graves of fallen soldiers.

Memorial Day was originally called Decoration Day.

After the Civil War, people from both the North and South decorated relatives' graves with flowers.

In 1882, the holiday was renamed Memorial Day.

Independence Day Flag Facts

Independence Day honors the signing of the Declaration of Independence.

John Hancock signed his name in very large handwriting. He wanted the King of England to be able to read it without his glasses.

The Liberty Bell is inscribed: Proclaim Liberty Throughout All the Land Unto All the Inhabitants Thereof.

The Declaration of Independence was signed by the Continental Congress on July 4, 1776.

The bell of Independence Hall was rung in honor of the signing of the Declaration of Independence. It was later named the Liberty Bell.

The first fourth of July took place on July 4, 1777. Fireworks are often used in fourth of July celebrations.

Flag Report

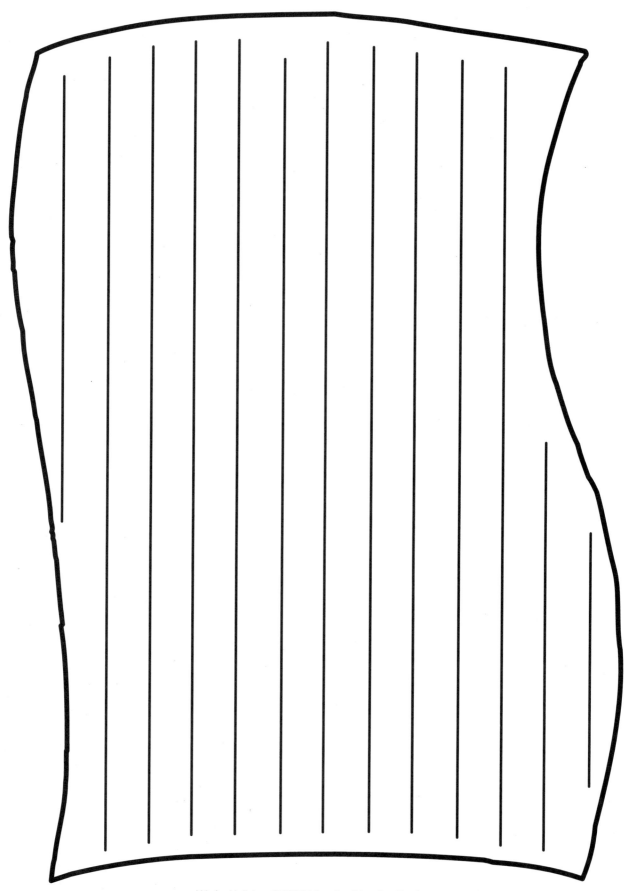

H Is for Holidays © 2002 Monday Morning Books

Independence Day Brochure

In celebration of Independence Day, the children will create brochures filled with information about America.

Materials:
Brochure Pattern (p. 50), pens or pencils, crayons or markers, resource books and encyclopedias

Preparation:
Duplicate a copy of the pattern for each child.

Directions:
1. Explain that the children will be making brochures that give information about the United States. They should pretend that people from other countries might look at the brochures to learn about the U.S.A.
2. Provide resource books and encyclopedias for children to use to gather information. Post the information listed on this page as starter facts.
3. Have the children illustrate their brochures. Then post the brochures where other classes can read them.

U.S.A. Information:
Capital: Washington D.C.
Motto: In God We Trust
National Anthem: Star-Spangled Banner
National Bird: Bald Eagle
National Flower: Rose

Brochure Pattern

Flags in a Row

This activity can be used for different levels of mathematical study. For younger children, write a plus or minus sign in the blank star. Write in a multiplication sign for older children.

Materials:
How Many Flags? (p. 52), pencils, crayons or markers

Preparation:
1. Fill in the missing signs (+, -, or x), then duplicate the How Many Flags? page. Make one for each child.
2. Make an answer key for self-checking, if desired.

Directions:
1. Give each child a copy of the math page.
2. Have the children do the problems and then share their answers with the class. Or they can use the answer key for self-checking.

Option:
To make the problems more difficult, white-out the numbers on the page and write in other numerals.

How Many Flags?

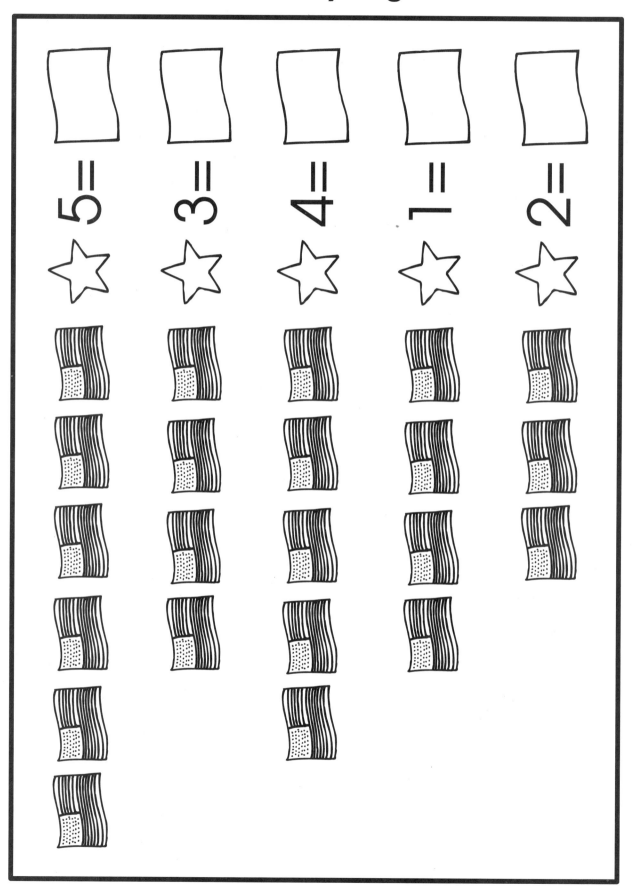

Boston Tea Party Spelling Bee

Materials:
Tea Bags (p. 54), Ship (p. 55), bag, scissors, colored markers, tape or glue

Preparation:
1. Duplicate a copy of the spelling words for each child and one for teacher use.
2. Cut the word patterns apart and color as desired.
3. Enlarge the pattern of the ship, color as desired, and post on a bulletin board. Add additional decorations to the board, if desired.

Directions:
1. Announce a date for a spelling "bee."
2. Divide the students into small groups. Have the children work together to learn the words. Let the children take the spelling words home to study.
3. On the day of the spelling bee, put the patterns in a bag. Pull one pattern from the bag at a time and have a child spell the word.
4. If the child spells the word correctly, he or she can post the word on the bulletin board. If not, another child tries to spell the word.
5. Continue until each child has a chance to spell one word, and all of the words are posted on the board.

Options:
• Use the blank tea bag to make enough words for each child in the classroom to spell at least one.
• If the words are too difficult, white-out the given spelling words and write in your own.

Tea Bag Patterns

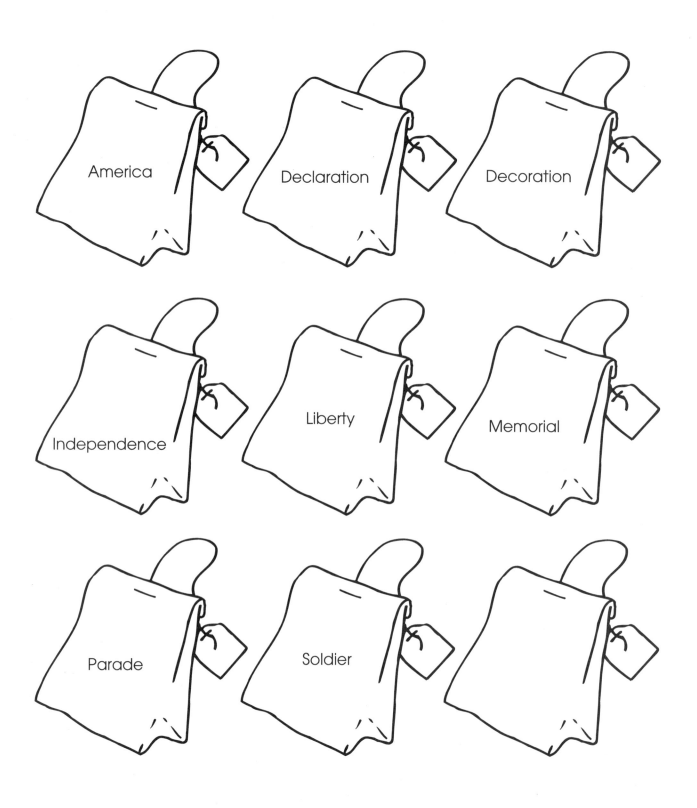

America

Declaration

Decoration

Independence

Liberty

Memorial

Parade

Soldier

Ship Pattern

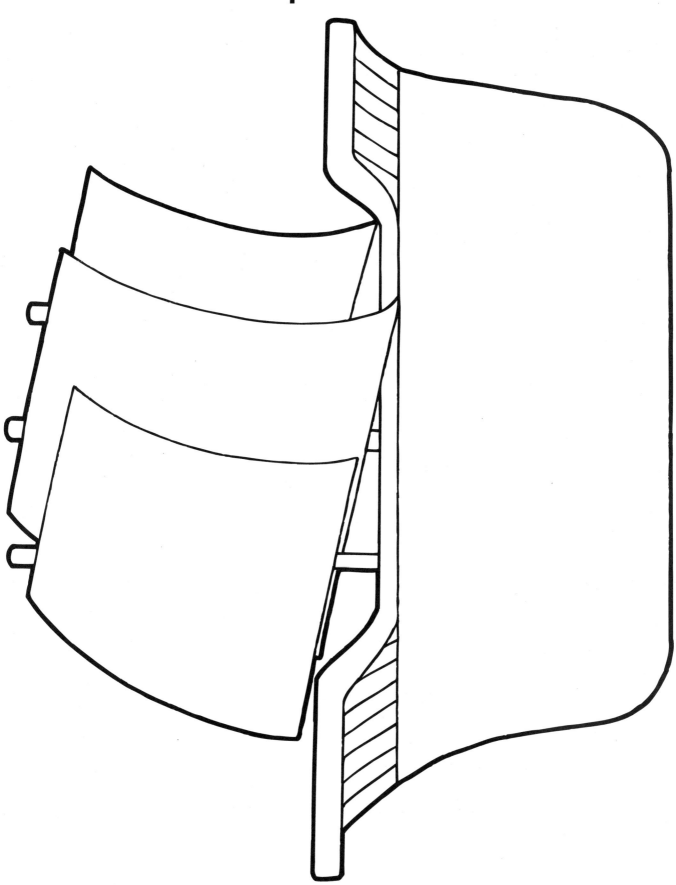

Paper Poppies

After World War I, Col. John McCrae wrote a poem (see p. 63) about soldiers buried in a poppy-filled French field. Several years later, a woman who had read the poem started the tradition of wearing poppies in tribute to soldiers on Memorial Day. Children can create their own paper flowers.

Materials:
Red tissue paper, green pipe cleaners, scissors, glue

Preparation:
None

Directions:
1. Have the children cut the tissue paper into circles.
2. Demonstrate how to gather the circles of tissue and twist in the center, to make the bottom of a flower.
3. Children wrap the pipe cleaner stems around the base of the flowers. They can glue the stems to the paper, if desired.
4. Gather the paper poppies and display throughout the classroom on Memorial Day.

Options:
• Have the children write their own poems to post with the poppies.
• Bring real poppies into the classroom for the children to observe.
• Duplicate the Paper Poppies patterns (p. 57) for children to color, cut out, and glue to pipe cleaner stems.

In Flanders Fields:
The poem begins with the following lines: "In Flanders fields the poppies blow, between the crosses, row on row..."

Paper Poppies

Who Wants to Be a Historian?

Children will challenge each other with multiple-choice questions to share what they know about history.

Materials:
Quiz Questions (p. 59), scissors, index cards, pencils, resource books about holidays and history

Preparation:
None

Directions:
1. Explain the game. You will read off a question and four possible answers. Children who think they know the answer will raise their hands. Choose one child to answer. If he or she is correct, let this child read the next question. If not, keep going until a child answers correctly.
2. Once the children understand the game, have each child create his or her own question with four possible answers. The children should write the question and answers on one side of an index card and the correct answer on the back. They can use information provided throughout this book, or from resource books or encyclopedias. Be sure to explain that three of the answers should be incorrect and only one will be correct.
3. Gather all of the children's questions and continue with the quiz game. Or let the children quiz each other.

Options:
• Let the children have a chance to remove two incorrect answers.
• Allow children to confer with a friend about the correct answer.

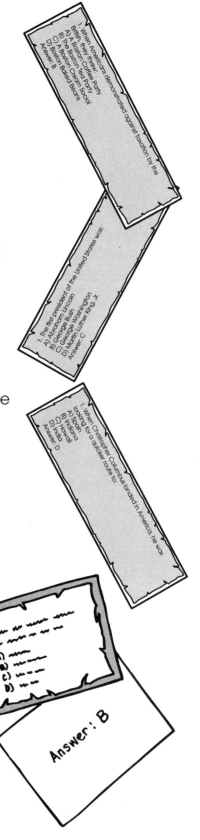

H Is for Holidays © 2002 Monday Morning Books

Quiz Questions

1. The first president of the United States was:
A) Abraham Lincoln
B) George Bush
C) George Washington
D) Martin Luther King, Jr.
Answer: C

2. When Christopher Columbus landed in America, he was looking for a quicker route to:
A) Spain
B) Indiana
C) Hawaii
D) India
Answer: D

3. When Americans demonstrated against taxation by the British, they threw:
A) A Boston Coffee Party
B) The Boston Tea Party
C) A Boston Cream Social
D) Boston Baked Beans
Answer: B

4. Martin Luther King, Jr. had a dream about:
A) A monster chasing him
B) Being elected President
C) Traveling to the moon
D) Equal rights for all people
Answer: D

5. Memorial Day honors:
A) People who like parades
B) The inventor of fireworks
C) Fallen soldiers
D) The Pilgrims
Answer: C

Independence Day Songs

John Hancock Signed His Name
(to the tune of "My Country 'Tis of Thee")

John Hancock signed his name
So large it gained him fame,
He had a plan.
He wrote his name with glee
So that King George could see
Now, was the time to set us free—
And give up this land.

I Think My Country's Great
(to the tune of "My Country 'Tis of Thee")

I think my country's great,
It really is first rate.
I'll tell you why—
We have our freedom, here.
We can speak anywhere,
Just listen, peace rings loud and clear
In America!

H Is for Holidays © 2002 Monday Morning Books

Flag Door Hangers

The United States flag changed several times throughout the past 200 years. Children can create their own flags for the new millennium.

Materials:
Door Hanger (p. 62), scissors, crayons or markers

Preparation:
Duplicate a copy of the pattern for each child.

Directions:
1. Give each child a pattern to cut out.
2. Have the children design their own flags on the door hangers.
3. The children can write their names on the flags and then take the hangers home to hang on their door knobs.

Option:
Post the flags in a classroom display before the children take them home.

Pattern

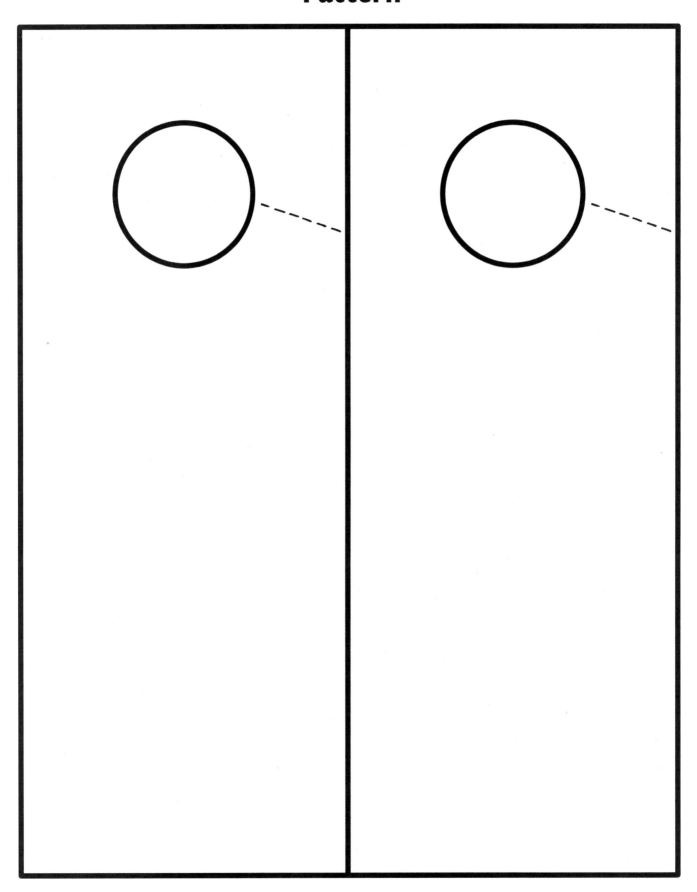

H Is for Holidays © 2002 Monday Morning Books

Resources

The Gettysburg Address was delivered by Abraham Lincoln on November 19, 1863 at the dedication of the cemetery at Gettysburg.

Four score and seven years ago our fathers brought forth on this continent, a new nation, conceived in Liberty, and dedicated to the proposition that all men are created equal.

Now we are engaged in a great civil war, testing whether that nation, or any nation so conceived and so dedicated, can long endure. We are met on a great battle-field of that war. We have come to dedicate a portion of that field, as a final resting place for those who here gave their lives that that nation might live. It is altogether fitting and proper that we should do this.

But, in a larger sense, we can not dedicate—we can not consecrate—we can not hallow—this ground. The brave men, living and dead, who struggled here, have consecrated it, far above our poor power to add or detract. The world will little note, nor long remember what we say here, but it can never forget what they did here. It is for us the living, rather, to be dedicated here to the unfinished work which they who fought here have thus far so nobly advanced. It is rather for us to be here dedicated to the great task remaining before us—that from these honored dead we take increased devotion to that cause for which they gave the last full measure of devotion—that we here highly resolve that these dead shall not have died in vain—that this nation, under God, shall have a new birth of freedom—and that government of the people, by the people, for the people, shall not perish from the earth.

"In Flanders Fields" (formerly, "We Shall Not Sleep")
In Flanders fields the poppies blow
Between the crosses, row on row.
That mark our place; and in the sky
The larks still bravely singing fly,
Scarce heard amidst the guns below.
We are the dead.
Short days ago we lived, felt dawn, saw sunset glow.
Loved and were loved, and now we lie
In Flanders fields.
Take up our quarrel with the foe,
To you from failing hands we throw
The Torch - be yours to hold it high;
If ye break faith with us who die
We shall not sleep though poppies grow
In Flanders fields."
—John McCrae

Name

HAS MASTERED

THE CONCEPT OF

HISTORY

AND IS AN HONORARY HISTORIAN

HONORARY HISTORIAN